# Audition Song Female Singers

## Beautiful

plus nine more hit songs
ideal for auditions

CW00326418

# Audition Songs for Female Singers
## Beautiful

plus nine more hit songs
ideal for auditions

THIS PUBLICATION IS NOT AUTHORISED FOR SALE IN
THE UNITED STATES OF AMERICA AND/OR CANADA.

**Wise Publications**
**part of The Music Sales Group**
London/New York/Paris/Sydney/Copenhagen/Berlin/Madrid/Tokyo

Published by
**Wise Publications**

Exclusive Distributors:
**Music Sales Limited**
8/9 Frith Street,
London W1D 3JB, England.
**Music Sales Pty Limited**
120 Rothschild Avenue,
Rosebery, NSW 2018,
Australia.

Order No. AM977130
ISBN 1-84449-026-2
This book © Copyright 2003 by Wise Publications

Unauthorised reproduction of any part of this publication by any
means including photocopying is an infringement of copyright.

Compiled by Nick Crispin.
Music arranged by Derek Jones.
Music processed by Paul Ewers Music Design.

CD recorded, mixed and mastered by Jonas Persson.
Backing tracks arranged by Danny G.
Lead and backing vocals by Elly Barnes.

Cover photograph (Christina Aguilera) courtesy London Features International.

Printed in the United Kingdom by
Caligraving Limited, Thetford, Norfolk.

**Your Guarantee of Quality**
As publishers, we strive to produce every book
to the highest commercial standards.
The music has been freshly engraved and the book has been
carefully designed to minimise awkward page turns and
to make playing from it a real pleasure.
Particular care has been given to specifying acid-free,
neutral-sized paper made from pulps which have not been
elemental chlorine bleached. This pulp is from farmed sustainable
forests and was produced with special regard for the environment.
Throughout, the printing and binding have been planned to ensure a
sturdy, attractive publication which should give years of enjoyment.
If your copy fails to meet our high standards, please inform us and
we will gladly replace it.

www.musicsales.com

# Beautiful

## Words & Music by Linda Perry

© COPYRIGHT 2001 FAMOUS MUSIC CORPORATION, USA.
ALL RIGHTS RESERVED. INTERNATIONAL COPYRIGHT SECURED.

(Don't look at me)     *Vocal ad lib.*

1. Ev - 'ry day__ is so
2. To all your friends__ you're de -

8

# Complicated

### Words & Music by Lauren Christy, David Alspach, Graeme Edwards & Avril Lavigne

© COPYRIGHT 2002 WARNER/CHAPPELL NORTH AMERICA LIMITED (75%)/
RONDOR MUSIC (LONDON) LIMITED (25%).
ALL RIGHTS RESERVED. INTERNATIONAL COPYRIGHT SECURED.

# Don't Know Why

## Words & Music by Jesse Harris

© COPYRIGHT 2002 BEANLY SONGS/SONY/ATV SONGS LLC, USA.
SONY/ATV MUSIC PUBLISHING (UK) LIMITED.
ALL RIGHTS RESERVED. INTERNATIONAL COPYRIGHT SECURED.

*Verse 3:*
Out across the endless se a
I will die in ecstasy
But I'll be a bag of bones
Driving down the road alone.

My heart is drenched in wine *etc.*

*Verse 4:*
Something has to make you run
I don't know why I didn't come.
My field is empty as a drum
I don't know why I didn't come,
I don't know why I didn't come,
I don't know why I didn't come.

# For What It's Worth

## Words & Music by Nina Persson & Peter Svensson

© COPYRIGHT 2003 STOCKHOLM SONGS, SWEDEN.
UNIVERSAL MUSIC PUBLISHING LIMITED.
ALL RIGHTS RESERVED. INTERNATIONAL COPYRIGHT SECURED.

# Kiss Kiss

## Words & Music by Aksu Sezen, Juliette Jaimes & Steve Welton-Jaimes

© COPYRIGHT 2001 UNIVERSAL MUSIC PUBLISHING LIMITED.
ALL RIGHTS RESERVED. INTERNATIONAL COPYRIGHT SECURED.

Mwah!

Mwah!

1. When you look at me, tell me what you see. This is what you get, it's the way I am.
*(Verse 2 see block lyric)*

you lose your head I'll find you, send-ing you my kiss. If you for-get I'll re-mind you, if

you're pa-ra-noid I'm be-hind you.__ If you lose your head I'll find you.__ Kiss

kiss.__ (Kiss kiss.) I, I. Ki - ki, I, I.

Mwah! Don't have to act like a... try - ing

Verse 2:
You could be mine baby, what's your star sign
Won't you take a step into the lions den?
I can hear my conscience calling me, calling me
Say'n I'm gonna be a bad girl again.
Why don't you come on over, we can't leave this all undone
Got a devil on my shoulder, there's no place for you to run.

You don't have to act *etc*.

# No More Drama

### Words & Music by Steven Lewis, James Harris, Barry DeVorzon & Perry Botkin

© COPYRIGHT 2000 FLYTE TYME TUNES.
SCREEN GEMS EMI MUSIC LIMITED.
ALL RIGHTS RESERVED. INTERNATIONAL COPYRIGHT SECURED.

# One Day I'll Fly Away

Words by Will Jennings
Music by Joe Sample

© COPYRIGHT 1980 IRVING MUSIC INCORPORATED/FOUR KNIGHTS MUSIC COMPANY, USA.
RONDOR MUSIC (LONDON) LIMITED (50%)/UNIVERSAL/MCA MUSIC LIMITED (50%).
ALL RIGHTS RESERVED. INTERNATIONAL COPYRIGHT SECURED.

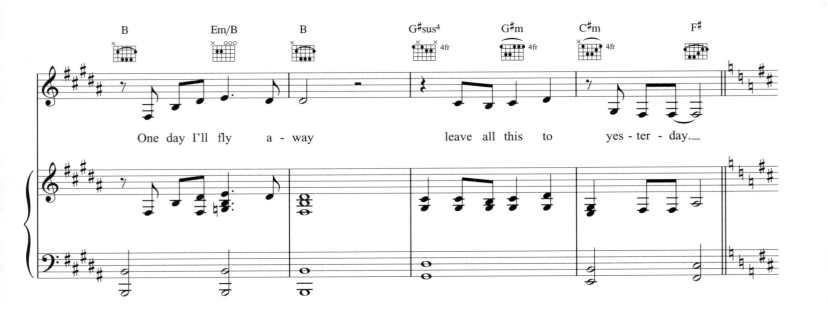

One day I'll fly a - way    leave all this to    yes - ter - day.

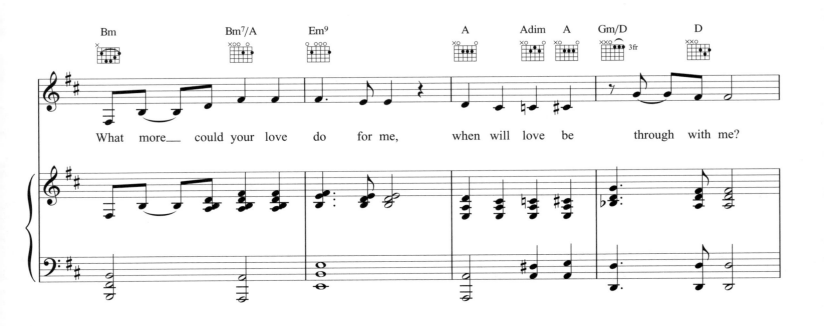

What more__ could your love do for me,    when will love be    through with me?

Why live life    from dream to dream,    and dread the day    when

dream - ing ends.

One day I'll fly___ a-way___ leave all this to

yes - ter - day.    Why live life from dream to dream,

and dread the day when dream - ing ends.

One day____ I'll fly a -

way    fly,    fly    a - way____

# A Thousand Miles

## Words & Music by Vanessa Carlton

© COPYRIGHT 2001 SONGS OF UNIVERSAL INCORPORATED/ROSASHARN PUBLISHING, USA.
UNIVERSAL MUSIC PUBLISHING LIMITED.
ALL RIGHTS RESERVED. INTERNATIONAL COPYRIGHT SECURED.

1,3. Mak-ing my way down town, walk-ing fast;
*(Verse 2 see block lyric)*

— fac-es pass,— and I'm home-bound.

47

*Verse 2:*
It's always times like these
When I think of you
And I wonder if you ever think of me.
'Cause everything's so wrong
And I don't belong
Living in your precious memory.
'Cause I need you
And I miss you
And now I wonder:

If I could fall into the sky *etc.*

# Whenever, Wherever

Words by Shakira & Gloria Estefan
Music by Shakira & Tim Mitchell

© COPYRIGHT 2002 ANIWI MUSIC LLC/SONY/ATV LATIN MUSIC PUBLISHING LLC/F.I.P.P. INTERNATIONAL, USA.
SONY/ATV MUSIC PUBLISHING (UK) LIMITED.
ALL RIGHTS RESERVED. INTERNATIONAL COPYRIGHT SECURED.

There's no-thing left to fear if you real-ly feel the way__ I__ feel.__

*Verse 2:*
Lucky that my lips not only mumble
They spill kisses like a fountain
Lucky that my breasts are small and humble
So you don't confuse them with mountains.
Lucky I have strong legs like my mother
To run for cover when I need it
And these two eyes are for no other
The day you leave will cry a river.
Le do le le le le, le do le le le le
At your feet, I'm at your feet.

Whenever, wherever *etc.*

# I'm Gonna Getcha Good!

## Words & Music by Shania Twain & Robert John "Mutt" Lange

© COPYRIGHT 2002 SONGS OF POLYGRAM INTERNATIONAL INCORPORATED/
LOON ECHO INCORPORATED/UNIVERSAL MUSIC PUBLISHING LIMITED (50%)/
OUT OF POCKET PRODUCTIONS LIMITED/ZOMBA MUSIC PUBLISHERS LIMITED (50%)
ALL RIGHTS RESERVED. INTERNATIONAL COPYRIGHT SECURED.

*To Coda* ⊕

*Verse 3:*
I've already planned it
Here's how it's gonna be
I'm gonna love you
And you're gonna fall in love with me, yeah.

So don't try to run. *etc.*

# More great book & CD song collections for auditions...

## Audition Songs for Female Singers

### Don't Cry For Me Argentina...
*plus* Adelaide's Lament, Big Spender; Heaven Help My Heart;
I Cain't Say No; I Will Survive; Out Here On My Own; Saving All My Love For You;
Someone To Watch Over Me; The Wind Beneath My Wings. ORDER NO. AM92587

### I Dreamed A Dream...
*plus* Another Suitcase In Another Hall; Fame; If I Were A Bell; Miss Byrd;
Save The Best For Last; Someone Else's Story; There Are Worse Things I Could Do;
What I Did For Love; You Can Always Count On Me. ORDER NO. AM950224

### Memory...
*plus* Can't Help Lovin' Dat Man; Crazy; Diamonds Are A Girl's Best Friend;
Now That I've Seen Her; Show Me Heaven; That Ole Devil Called Love;
The Winner Takes It All; Wishing You Were Somehow Here Again;
The Reason. ORDER NO. AM955284

### I Don't Know How To Love Him...
*plus* As Long As He Needs Me; Constant Craving; Feeling Good;
I Say A Little Prayer; If My Friends Could See Me Now;
It's Oh So Quiet; Killing Me Softly With His Song; Tell Me It's Not True;
You Must Love Me. ORDER NO. AM955295

### Chart Hits
Against All Odds (Take A Look At Me Now); American Pie; ...Baby One More Time;
Breathless; It Feels So Good; Man! I Feel Like A Woman; My Love Is Your Love;
Pure Shores; Rise; Sing It Back. ORDER NO. AM963765

### 90's Hits
History Repeating; I Will Always Love You; Never Ever; Perfect Moment;
Search For The Hero; That Don't Impress Me Much; Torn; 2 Become 1;
What Can I Do; You Gotta Be. ORDER NO. AM963776

### Hits of the 90s
All Mine; Baby One More Time; Black Velvet; Chains; Don't Speak;
From A Distance; Hero; Lovefool; Road Rage; What Can I Do. ORDER NO. AM966658

### Blues
Cry Me A River; Black Coffee; Fine And Mellow (My Man Don't Love Me);
The Lady Sings The Blues; Lover Man (Oh Where Can You Be) God Bless' The Child;
Moonglow; Natural Blues; Please Send Me Someone To Love; Solitude. ORDER NO. AM966669

### Classic Soul
Don't Make Me Over; I Just Want To Make Love To You; Midnight Train To Georgia;
Nutbush City Limits; Private Number; Rescue me; Respect; Son Of A Preacher Man;
Stay With Me Baby; (Take A Little) Piece Of My Heart. ORDER NO. AM966670

### R&B Hits
Ain't It Funny; AM To PM; Family Affair; Freak Like Me; Get The Party Started;
How Come You Don't Call Me; Shoulda Woulda Coulda; Sweet Baby; Survivor;
What About Us? ORDER NO. AM967351

## Audition Songs for Kids
Any Dream Will Do; Consider Yourself; I'd Do Anything; No Matter What;
Spice Up Your Life; Thank You For The Music; The Candy Man; Tomorrow;
When I'm Sixty Four. ORDER NO. AM955273

## More Audition Songs for Kids
The Bare Necessities; Can You Feel The Love Tonight; Food, Glorious Food;
Happy Talk; I Have A Dream; Maybe; Reach; Starlight Express; What If;
You've Got A Friend In Me. ORDER NO. AM966636

## Audition Songs for Male Singers

### Tonight...
*plus* All Good Gifts; Anthem; Being Alive; Corner Of The Sky; Funny;
High Flying, Adored; If I Loved You; Luck Be A Lady;
Why, God, Why? ORDER NO. AM92586

### Maria...
*plus* All I Need Is The Girl; Bring Him Home; Frederick's Aria;
I Don't Remember Christmas; Sit Down, You're Rocking The Boat;
Some Enchanted Evening; This Is The Moment; Where I Want To Be;
You're Nothing Without Me. ORDER NO. AM950213

### Angels...
*plus* Come What May; Is You Is Or Is You Ain't My Baby?; The Music Of The Night;
No Matter What; Reet Petite; Shoes Upon The Table; This Year's Love;
Try A Little Tenderness; Your Song. ORDER NO. AM972400

### Perfect Day...
*plus* Can You Feel The Love Tonight; Can't Take My Eyes Off You;
Flying Without Wings; The Great Pretender; I Can't Make You Love Me;
I Drove All Night; Let Me Entertain You; Light My Fire;
A Little Less Conversation; Trouble. ORDER NO. AM976085

## Audition Songs for Male & Female Singers

### Gilbert & Sullivan
I Am The Very Model Of A Modern Major-General; I'm Called Little Buttercup;
The Nightmare Song (When You're Lying Awake With A Dismal Headache);
On A Tree By A River (Wilow, Tit Willow); Poor Wand'ring One!;
Silvered Is The Raven Hair; The Sun Whose Rays Are All Ablaze;
Take A Pair Of Sparkling Eyes; When All Night A Chap Remains;
When Maiden Loves She Sits And Sighs. ORDER NO. AM958188

### Christmas Hits
Fairytale Of New York; Happy Xmas (War Is Over);
I Wish It Could Be Christmas Every Day; Last Christmas; Lonely This Christmas;
Merry Xmas Everybody; Mistletoe And Wine; A Spaceman Came Travelling;
Step Into Christmas; Wonderful Christmastime. ORDER NO. AM971586

### Christmas Ballads
Baby, It's Cold Outside; Blue Christmas; C.H.R.I.S.T.M.A.S.;
The Christmas Song (Chestnuts Roasting On An Open Fire); The Christmas Waltz;
Home For The Holidays; I Saw Mommy Kissing Santa Claus;
Let It Snow! Let It Snow! Let It Snow!; Santa Baby. ORDER NO. AM85465

# Special 176-page double-CD compilations...

## Professional Singers Audition Book
Thirty-eight essential audition songs for women. ORDER NO. AM966680

## Audition Songs for Professinal Singers
Features over 30 great chart hits for women. ORDER NO. AM974578

ALL TITLES AVAILABLE FROM GOOD MUSIC RETAILERS OR, IN CASE OF DIFFICULTY, CONTACT
MUSIC SALES LIMITED, NEWMARKET ROAD, BURY ST. EDMUNDS, SUFFOLK IP33 3YB
TELEPHONE: 01284 725725; FAX: 01284 702592
WWW.MUSICSALES.COM

# CD Track Listing

To remove your CD from the plastic sleeve, lift the small
lip on the right to break the perforated flap.
Replace the disc after use for convenient storage.